P9-ECA-466

Let's Explore with Cor Cor

Written By: Cory Lee & Sandy Gilbreath

Illustrated By: Amanuel Moore

Keep exploring!
Sandy Gilbreath
&
[illegible]

This book is dedicated to:

Every kid that has ever been told they can't do something just because they are in a wheelchair. With enough determination, you can do anything!

This is Cor Cor.
Cor Cor is not able to walk,
but this doesn't stop him
from traveling the world.

Cor Cor uses a wheelchair to
move himself around,
But don't think for a minute that
he is wheelchair-bound.
He loves to roll fast as he travels
to a new place.
Speeding around the globe puts a
big smile upon his face.

Cor Cor can fly in an airplane
with birds all around.

Cor Cor can ride on a train
all through the town.

KERY

Cor Cor can even ride in a boat
across the deep blue sea.

And Cor Cor can ride in a hot air balloon
high above a tree.

The world is a great big place
and there are so many things to see.
Cor Cor can have fun too,
just like you and me.

He can go on a safari ride in Africa
and see all the animals oh so near.

Cor Cor can go to Finland
and see Santa's lovely reindeer.

S
S

Cor Cor can go to Florida
and ride a special chair
across the sand.

Or he can go to a concert
and hear his favorite band.

Cor Cor can travel to Australia
and take a ferry to his favorite zoo.
This is always so fun
because he can pet a kangaroo.

He can take a plane ride to Iceland
and see the Northern Lights.
Oh, there is so much to see.
There are many, many sights.

Cor Cor can go to London
and ride the London Eye.
His pod will go around and around
way up in the sky.
He can see Tower Bridge and look...
there's Big Ben!
His wheels are always moving,
always rolling again and again.

Cor Cor just can't sit still.
There's so much to see and do.
So, where is your next adventure?
There's nothing stopping you!

About the Authors

Cory Lee and Sandy Gilbreath are the mother-son duo behind the award-winning travel blog, Curb Free with Cory Lee. After Cory's diagnosis of Spinal Muscular Atrophy and becoming a wheelchair user at the age of 4, Sandy raised him with the motto “If you can’t stand up, stand out!” Since then, they have traveled to all 7 continents and several dozen countries together. They hope that this book inspires others, both those with disabilities and without, to break out of their comfort zones and see the world! Learn more about Cory and Sandy at CurbFreeWithCoryLee.com

About the Illustrator

Amanuel Moore has always had a passion for drawing and painting, and he is excited to make his professional debut as a children’s book illustrator with *Lets Explore with Cor Cor*. Amanuel is a loving father of two, Ashton and Kylan. He is looking forward to seeing where this new journey takes him!

CPSIA information can be obtained at www.ICGtesting.com
Printed in the USA
BVIW121113140720
582570BV00003B/2